What I Wish for

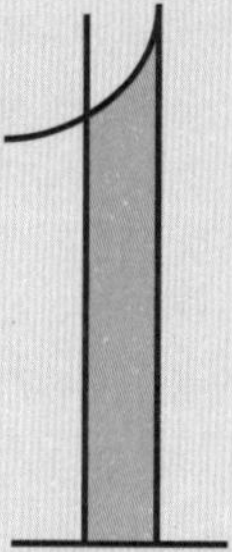

I wish I could give you a

____.

2

I wish the world knew about your

____.

3

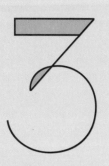

I wish we could

____

together one day.

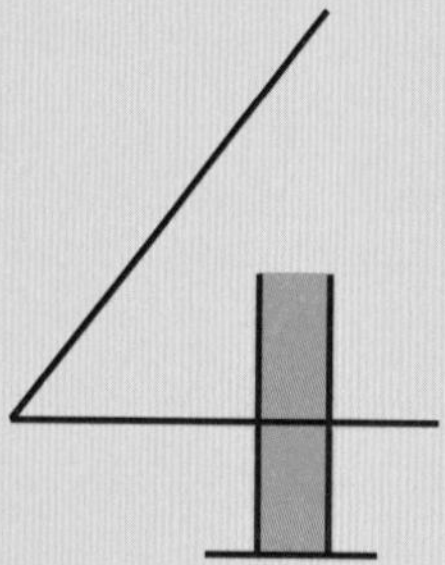
4

I wish I were as good as you at

____.

5

I wish I had known you when

____ .

6

You are my favorite

____

in the world.

7

I wish more people could

____

your

____.

8

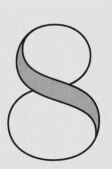

I wish you'd start

____.

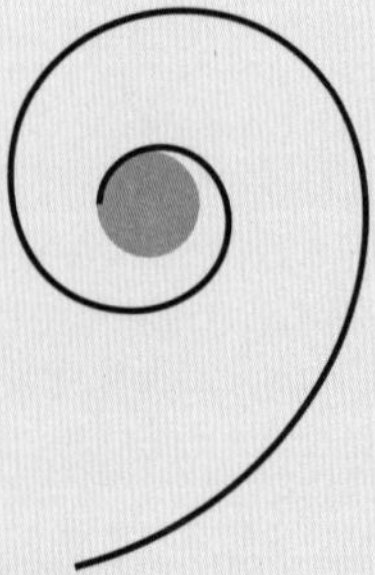

I wish you'd stop

____ .

10

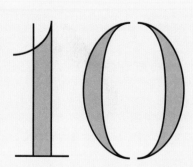

I wish I could bottle and sell your

______________________________ .

11

If you were a city, you'd be

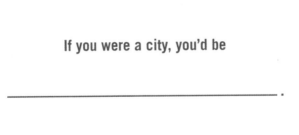

______________________________________.

12

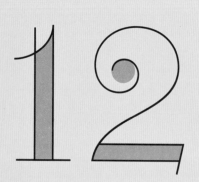

I wish you knew how much I

you.

13

I wish we could play

____

every

______________________________.

14

I wish we could go

____

again.

15

I wish the world had more of your unique

____ .

16

I hope you get to

____

someday.

17

I wish your

____

appreciated how

____

you are.

18

I wish we were

____

right now.

19

I wish you'd show me how to

____.

20

I believe we'd make a great

____

team.

21

I wish you were flying to

tonight.

22

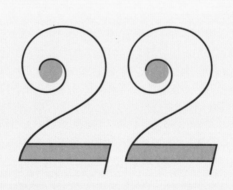

I wish you weren't always right about

_______________________________________.

23

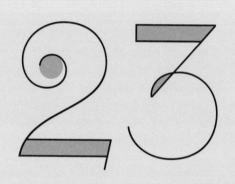

It would make me happy if you could

____

whenever you wanted.

24

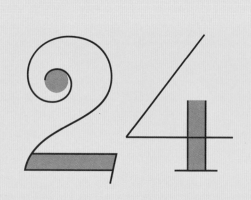

I wish I knew your secret for

____.

25

I wish I could make your

____

go away.

26

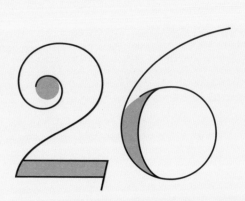

I wish someone would

____

a

____

about you.

27

Sometimes, I wish you'd never have to

____

again.

28

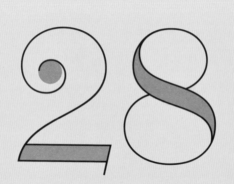

It's fun to

____

with you.

29

I wish we were still

____.

30

You deserve the

____

award.

31

I wish you'd let me

____

for you.

32

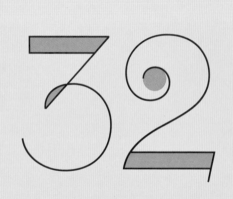

I wish your

____

could be studied by science.

33

I wish you weren't so good at giving me

____ .

34

If you were a drink, you'd be

____ .

35

I wish I had your taste in

____.

36

I wish I could buy you that

____

you want.

37

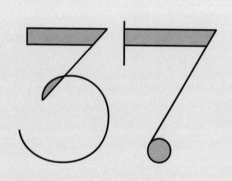

I hope you get to

your favorite

soon.

38

I'd rather

____

with you than anyone else.

39

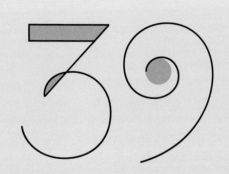

I wish I could get you

____

right now.

40

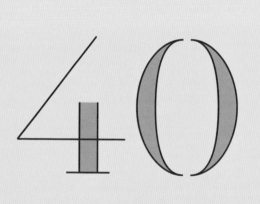

I hope you never forget that I

____.

41

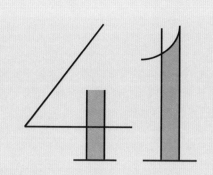

If I could grant you one wish it'd be

____.

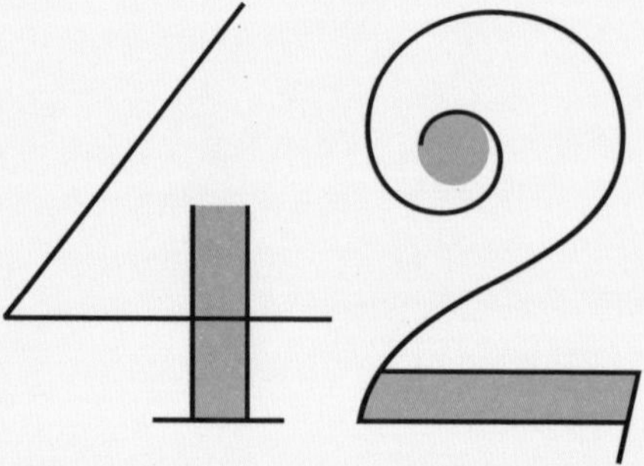
42

I wish everybody were as

____

as you.

43

If you were an instrument, you'd be

______________________________________.

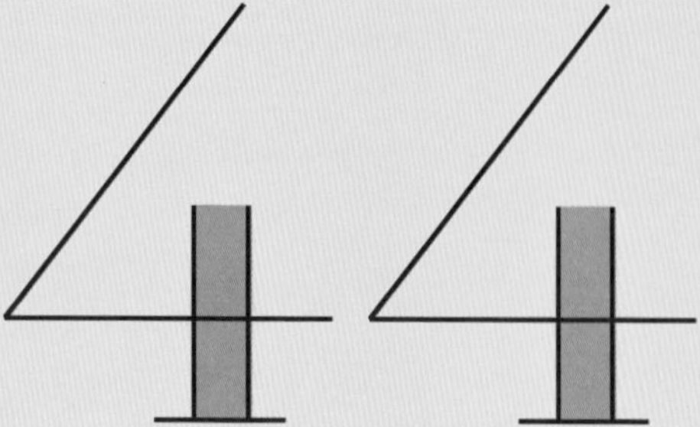
44

I wish I had your

____.

45

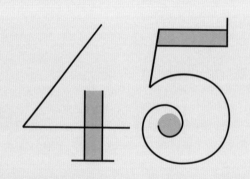

I wish you weren't so darn

____.

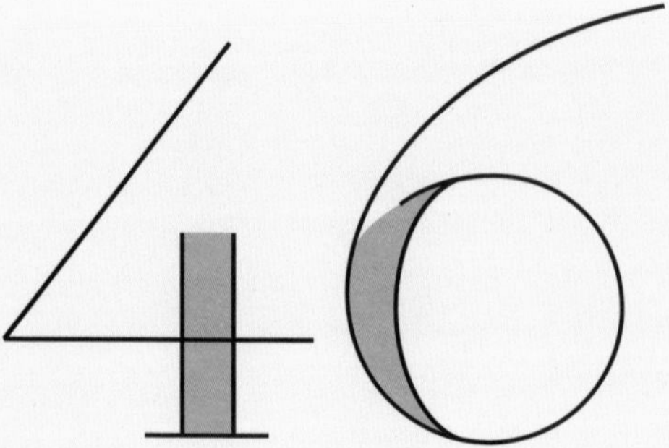
46

I hope to see you

one day.

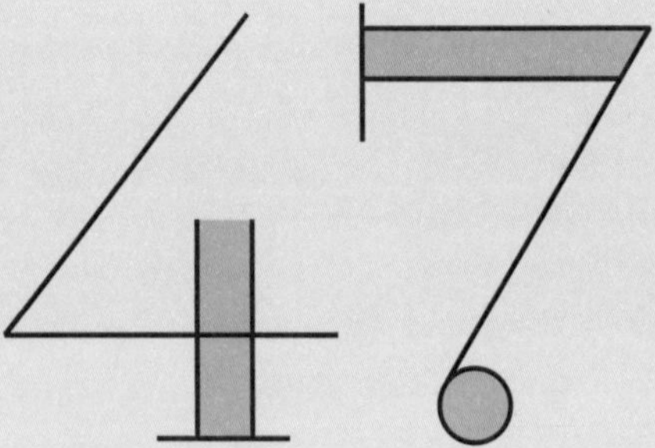
47

I wish you'd feel free to

____

more often.

48

It's hard to put into words how much I wish

____.

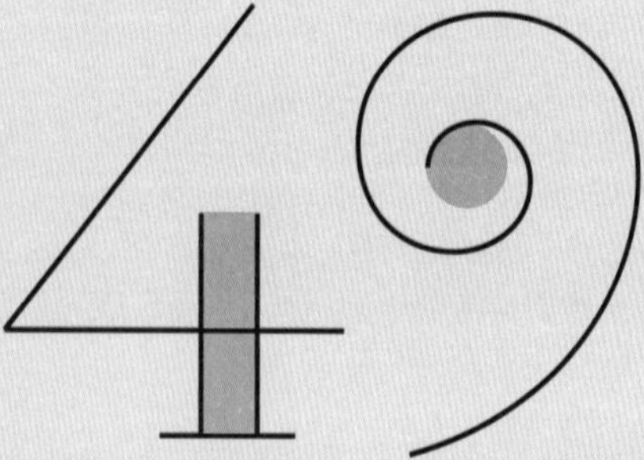
49

I hope our

____

lasts forever.

50

I wish you all the

____

on the planet.

I Wish You All Good Things.

Fill in the *Love*.®

Created, published, and distributed by Knock Knock
1635-B Electric Ave.
Venice, CA 90291
knockknockstuff.com
Knock Knock is a registered trademark of Knock Knock LLC
Fill in the Love is a registered trademark of Knock Knock LLC

Made in China

ISBN: 978-160106925-2
UPC: 825703-50255-8
10 9 8 7 6 5 4 3 2 1